SHOWSTOPPERS

WISE PUBLICATIONS
PART OF THE MUSIC SALES GROUP

LONDON / NEW YORK / PARIS / SYDNEY / COPENHAGEN / BERLIN / MADRID / TOKYO

PUBLISHED BY
WISE PUBLICATIONS
8/9 FRITH STREET, LONDON, W1D 3JB, ENGLAND.

EXCLUSIVE DISTRIBUTORS:
MUSIC SALES LIMITED
DISTRIBUTION CENTRE, NEWMARKET ROAD, BURY ST EDMUNDS,
SUFFOLK, IP33 3YB, ENGLAND.
MUSIC SALES PTY LIMITED
120 ROTHSCHILD AVENUE, ROSEBERY, NSW 2018, AUSTRALIA.

ORDER NO. AM982784
ISBN 1-84609-043-1
THIS BOOK © COPYRIGHT 2005 BY WISE PUBLICATIONS,
A DIVISION OF MUSIC SALES LIMITED.

ARRANGING AND ENGRAVING SUPPLIED BY CAMDEN MUSIC.

Beauty And The Beast

Lyrics by Howard Ashman. Music by Alan Menken

After a long tradition of filming broadway musicals, Disney decided to reverse the trend and make a broadway musical from their smash film. It is the only animated film to get an Academy Award nomination for Best Picture.

Hints & Tips: Make sure the quavers (eighth notes) are rhythmical all the way through. Think carefully about the note your right hand thumb needs to be on—it's not the same all the way through.

ALADDIN
A Whole New World

Music by Alan Menken. Lyrics by Tim Rice

The familiar pantomime story given a modern Disney twist. The dazzling princess Jasmine has led a life of seclusion and longs to see the city outside her palace. This is the duet Aladdin and Jasmine sing when they fall in love.

Hints & Tips: Don't forget that the key signature is F major, which means, remember the B♭s. Also, notice that the left hand has important material too, e.g. bars 10 and 18.

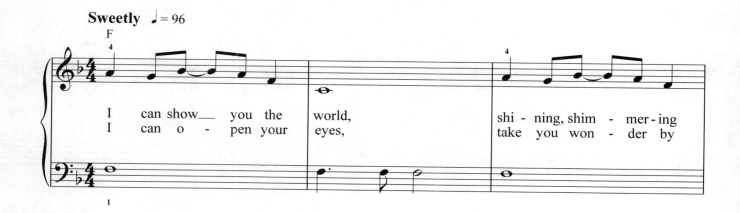

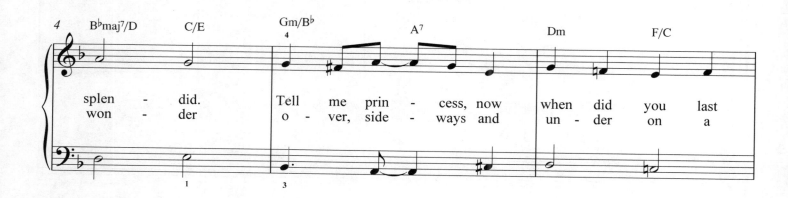

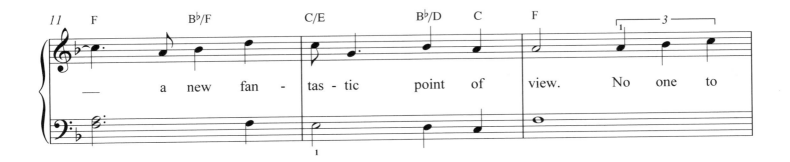

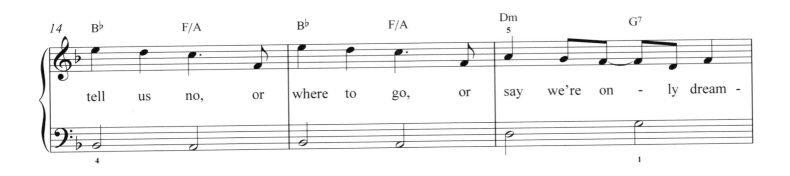

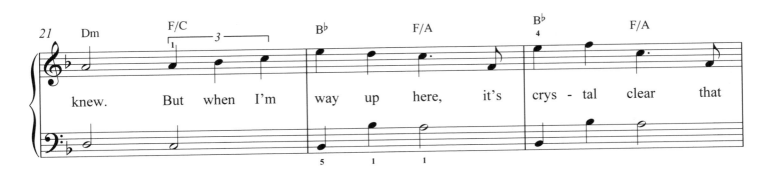

BLOOD BROTHERS

Tell Me It's Not True

Words & Music by Willy Russell

The bloody finale of the tale of twin brothers who are separated as babies. The work follows their lives as they grow up as friends without knowledge of their kinship. The difference in their upbringing leads to jealousy and tragedy.

Hints & Tips: Pay careful attention to the frequent changes of time signature. Watch that the semiquavers (sixteenth notes) are played at the correct tempo. Lastly, remember the D.C. (Da Capo), which instructs you to repeat back to the beginning.

Slowly and sadly

Cabaret

Words by Fred Ebb. Music by John Kander

Cabaret opened on Broadway on 20 November 1966 and ran for no less than 1,165 performances. The story describes the decadence of the Weimar Republic just before Hitler's rise to power.

Hints & Tips: Although this piece is in 2/2 time, it's best to count four until you know it. The rhythm of the tune in bar 1 appears many times, so it's important to get it right. Counting four, play one-two/three-four, the middle note of the three (minim/half note) being held for two counts. Make sure you know what the D.C. al Coda means.

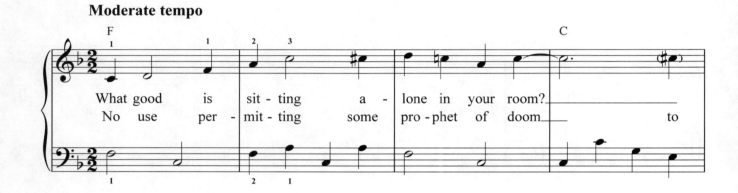

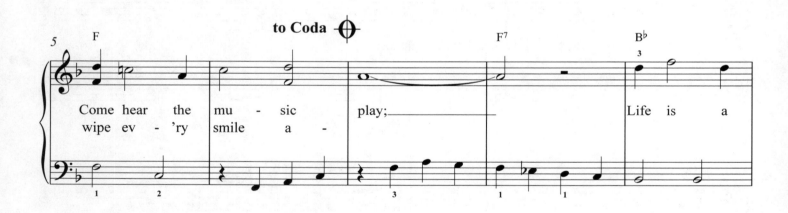

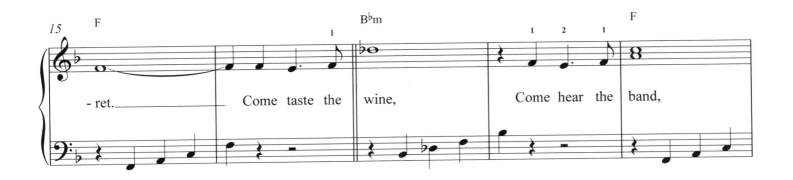

-ret._____ Come taste the wine, Come hear the band,

D.C. al Coda

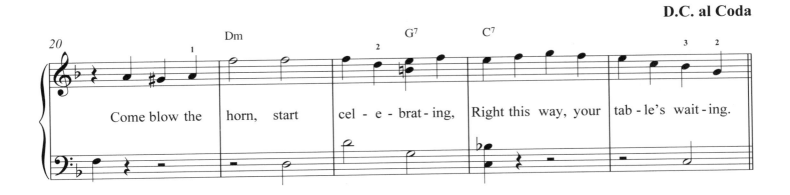

Come blow the horn, start cel - e - brat - ing, Right this way, your tab - le's wait - ing.

✠ **Coda**

-way._____ Life is a cab - a -

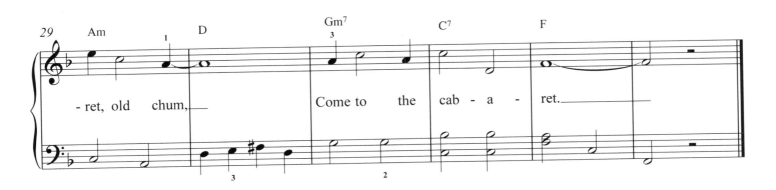

-ret, old chum,___ Come to the cab - a - ret.

9

CATS

Memory

Music by Andrew Lloyd Webber. Lyrics by Trevor Nunn after T.S. Eliot

Adapted from T.S. Eliot's set of poems entitled *Old Possum's Book Of Practical Cats*. Grizabella sings this song wishing she could be born again and relive her old life.

Hints & Tips: The left hand arpeggios should be quite gentle and should have a rippling feel. Make sure that you observe the time signature change in bar 10; the quavers (eighth notes) will feel slower.

D.C. al Coda

Coda

rit.

One

Words by Edward Kleban. Music by Marvin Hamlisch

This show ran for nearly 15 years on Broadway. The story focuses on a group of dancers who are all determined to make the 'cut' for a Broadway show. *One* is a big chorus number about the qualities one needs to stand out from the crowd.

Hints & Tips: This piece is not easy, and will benefit from slow practice to accommodate the many accidentals. Play the dotted rhythms crisply to create a bouncy feel to the music. Play the triplets in bar 7 smoothly and perfectly in time.

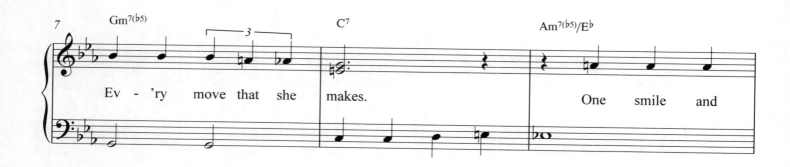

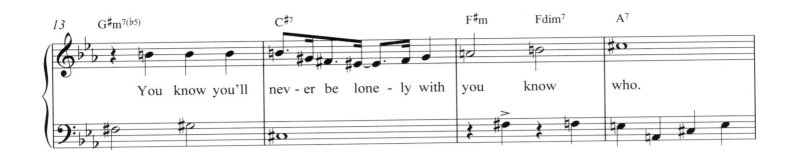

You know you'll nev - er be lone - ly with you know who.

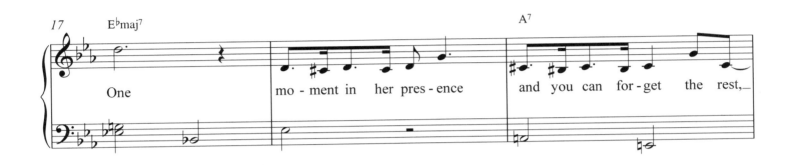

One mo - ment in her pres - ence and you can for - get the rest,

for the girl is sec - ond best to none,

son. Ooh! Sigh! Give her your at - ten - tion. Do I

real - ly have to men - tion, she's the one?

Don't Cry For Me Argentina

Music by Andrew Lloyd Webber. Lyrics by Tim Rice

Based on the real life struggle for power, and the life of Eva Duarte (Evita), this musical was turned into a star-studded film with Madonna in the lead role in 1996.

Hints & Tips: The crotchet (quarter note) triplets are quite tricky to fit with the LH. Think of the lyrics to help you. The left hand plays an accompaniment, so be sure to bring out the melody in the right hand.

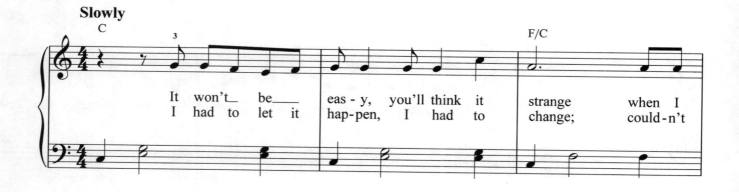

If I Were A Rich Man

Words by Sheldon Harnick. Music by Jerry Bock

A story about a philosophical dairy farmer, Tevye, played by Topol in the film, who strives to maintain traditional Jewish values in the face of oppression from the Tsarist Russian Orthodoxy. In this song Tevye wishes he was a man of leisure and influence in the community.

Hints & Tips: Try to create the right feel (or mood) by playing the staccato notes crisply. Watch out for the unusual accidentals.

right in the mid-dle of the town; a fine tin roof with real wood-en floors be -

-low. There would be one long stair - case just go - ing up and

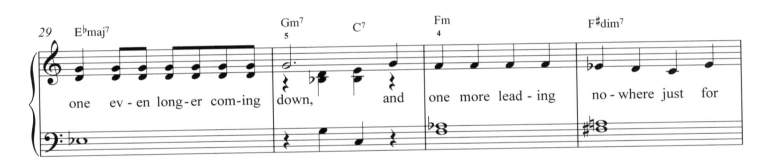

one ev - en long-er com-ing down, and one more lead - ing no - where just for

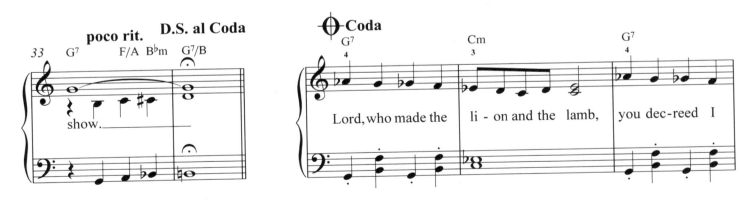

show.____ Lord, who made the li - on and the lamb, you dec-reed I

should be what I am; would it spoil some vast e - ter-nal plan, if I were a wealth-y man?

Matchmaker

Words by Sheldon Harnick. Music by Jerry Bock

Tevye's daughters wonder who the Matchmaker, Yente will bring to marry them. The film version of this classic musical picked up three Academy Awards in 1971.

Hints & Tips: The dotted minims (dotted half notes) must be held for a full three beats. Some bars of the right hand have two voices (parts)—make sure that your audience hears the upper part more clearly.

Luck Be A Lady

Words & Music by Frank Loesser

The song that Sky Masterson sings just as he is about to bet thousands of dollars on the outcome of a single dice throw. In the film of this musical, the leads of Nathan Detroit and Sky Masterson were taken by Frank Sinatra and Marlon Brando.

Hints & Tips: There are some tricky accidentals in this piece; perhaps they could be circled in pencil to help you to remember! The sign over the last note is an accent which means it should be strongly emphasised.

Superstar

Music by Andrew Lloyd Webber. Lyrics by Tim Rice

The character Judas sings this taunting song about the failure of Christ's mission from his own guilt for betraying his master. *Jesus Christ Superstar* is a rock opera and shows how far music theatre has progressed from its origins in vaudeville.

Hints & Tips: The semiquavers (sixteenth notes) form part of an important rhythmic figure. Think of the lyrics of the song to help you play the figure correctly.

JOSEPH AND THE AMAZING TECHNICOLOR® DREAMCOAT

Close Every Door

Music by Andrew Lloyd Webber. Lyrics by Tim Rice

The show that gave rise to the careers of both Tim Rice and Andrew Lloyd Webber. The show had humble beginnings when in 1967, Lloyd Webber was asked to provide a pop cantata for his brother's school concert.

Hints & Tips: Pay close attention to the bars in which the left hand has important musical material (e.g. bars 8, 9, 11 etc.) These should be clearly heard. Also, there are lots of crescendi, diminuendi, and hairpins to observe.

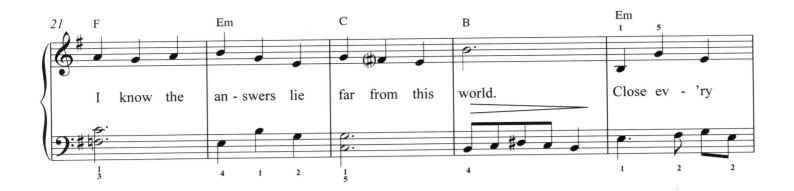

21 | F | Em | C | B | Em

I know the an-swers lie far from this world. Close ev - 'ry

26 | B⁷ | Em | B⁷ | Em | Cmaj⁷

door to me, keep those I love from me; chil-dren of Is - rael are

31 | Am⁶ | B | G | C | D G D⁷/A

nev - er a - lone. For I know I shall find my___ own peace of

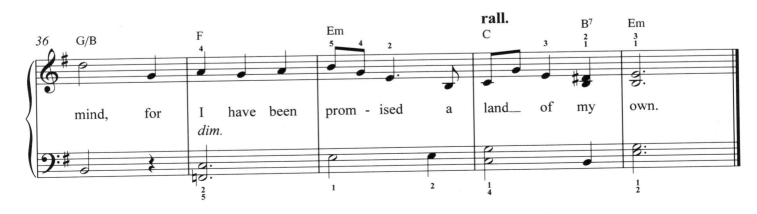

rall.

36 | G/B | F | Em | C B⁷ | Em

mind, for I have been prom - ised a land__ of my own.

dim.

THE JUNGLE BOOK

The Bare Necessities

Words & Music by Terry Gilkyson

Baloo the bear meets the man cub, Mowgli, and gets him to loosen up a little and go with the flow in this song from the Disney story adapted from Rudyard Kipling's book.

Hints & Tips: Follow the words of the song to help you with the tied rhythms. Make this piece bouncy and bright by playing staccato. 2/2 means two beats in the bar, but it's best to count four, and play much slower, until you know the music.

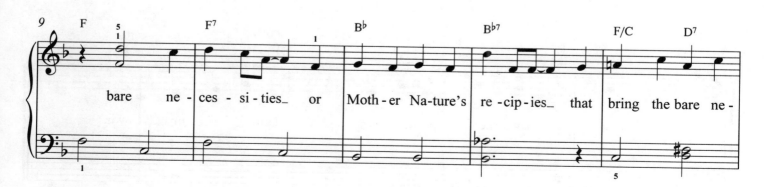

© Copyright 1964 Wonderland Music Company, Inc.
All Rights Reserved. International Copyright Secured.

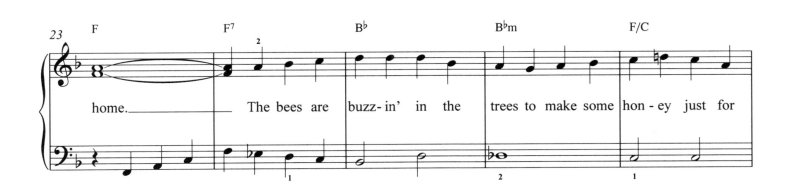

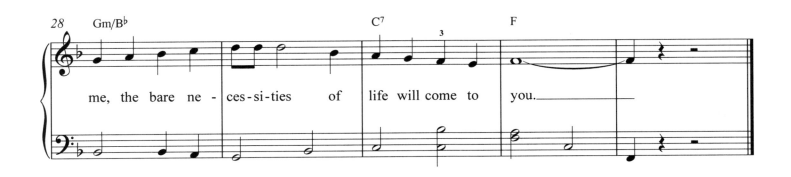

On My Own

Music by Claude-Michel Schönberg. Original Lyrics by Alain Boublil & Jean-Marc Natel.
English Lyrics by Herbert Kretzmer, Trevor Nunn & John Caird

The lovestruck Eponine sings of her unrequited love for Marius, the student revolutionary. Despite a warning, Eponine returns to the Barricade, is wounded and dies in Marius' arms.

Hints & Tips: In this piece there are plenty of dotted rhythms and time signature changes to observe. The middle section (bars 10–17) is full of tricky accidentals. Make sure that the semiquavers (sixteenth notes) are equal in speed and in volume.

D.S. al Coda

Coda

Circle Of Life

Music by Elton John. Lyrics by Tim Rice

The opening number from the Disney smash hit film of 1994. More commonly known for his pop records, Elton John teamed up with Tim Rice in Elton's first film soundtrack since 1971.

Hints & Tips: The rhythm in bar 7 (repeated in bar 16) is quite tricky. Try practising the right hand alone whilst counting a bar of 4/4 aloud.

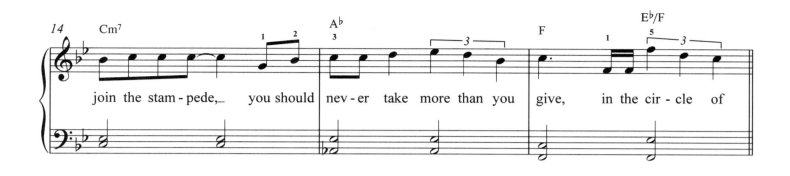

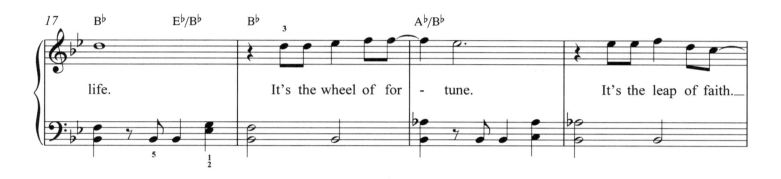

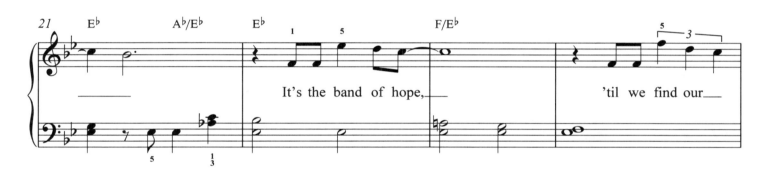

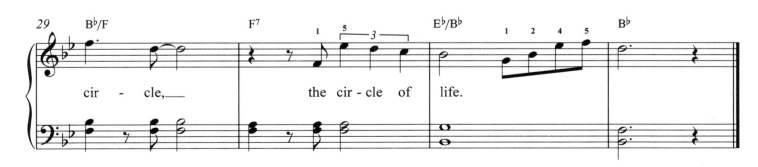

The Last Night Of The World

Music by Claude-Michel Schönberg. Lyrics by Alain Boublil & Richard Maltby Jr.
Adapted from original French Lyrics by Alain Boublil

Miss Saigon was inspired by the same play that inspired Puccini to write *Madama Butterfly*.
To date the show has been seen in 138 cities worldwide.

Hints & Tips: Take care with the leaps in the melody in the second part of this piece. If you find the tied rhythms difficult, practise them first without the ties. Then when you are confident with the music, try again, replacing the ties.

Who Will Buy?

Words & Music by Lionel Bart

Adapted from Charles Dickens' classic novel, *Oliver Twist*. The composer of the show, Lionel Bart, was never able to repeat the success he enjoyed with *Oliver!* and by the seventies he was virtually bankrupt.

Hints & Tips: This is quite a quick song, but it's important to practise it slowly first. Notice that the first three phrases of the song start on the second beat. Always play this note strongly, to reinforce this rhythm. Make sure you know which notes make up the three-flat key signature.

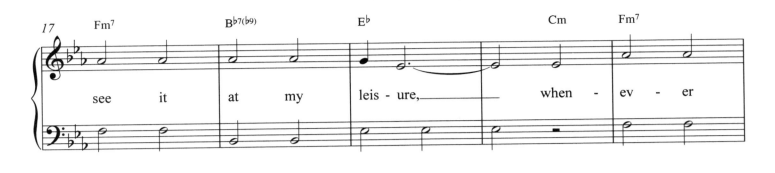

see it at my leis-ure,___ when-ev---er

things go wrong, and I would keep it as a

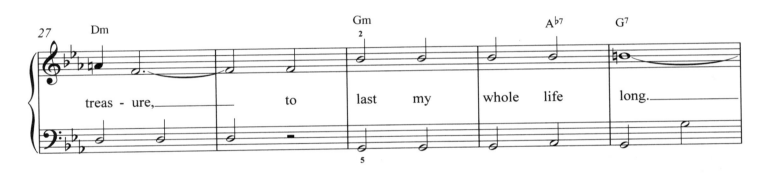

treas-ure,___ to last my whole life long.___

D.C. al Coda

Coda
Slower

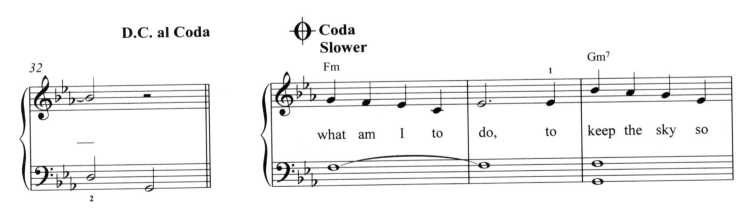

what am I to do, to keep the sky so

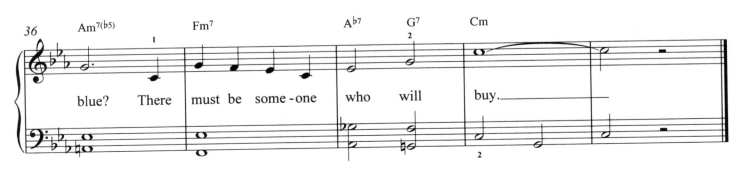

blue? There must be some-one who will buy.___

The Phantom Of The Opera

Music by Andrew Lloyd Webber. Words by Charles Hart

This musical is based on a 1911 novel by French writer Gaston Leroux. The story concerns a composer whose disfigured face drives him to shun the everyday world in favour of the vast cavernous cellars of the Paris Opera.

Hints & Tips: The left hand should remain equal in tone and length throughout. Try to relax your left hand wrist! Make sure also that the semibreves (whole notes) are held for their full length.

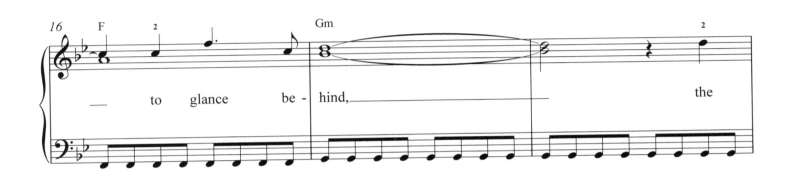

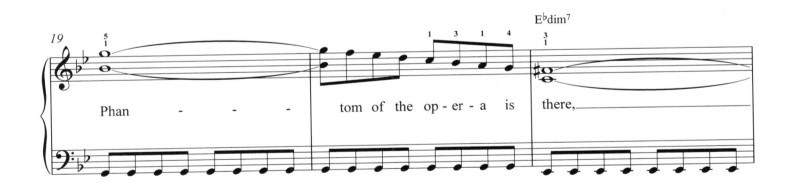

The Time Warp

Words & Music by Richard O'Brien

A wacky rock musical spoof, loosely based on the horror story, *Frankenstein*. Richard O'Brien has said that Dr. Frankenfurter, the main character, was based on a mix of Sergei Eisenstein's Ivan the Terrible and Cruella DeVil.

Hints & Tips: The rhythm in the left hand in bar 1 is an important element in this piece. Notice the 5-2 finger stretch always occurs with this rhythm—be aware that you are stretching an extra note between the fingers. Use the rhythm of the words to help you with your timing.

Medium rock beat

38

SHOWBOAT

Can't Help Lovin' Dat Man

Words by Oscar Hammerstein II. Music by Jerome Kern

Showboat made history in the late twenties for being the first broadway musical to deal with issues of racism and marital heartbreak. Oscar Hammerstein II would revisit the epic nature and depth of story telling in this show with his long term collaborator Richard Rodgers many years later.

Hints & Tips: Always remember to carefully check accidentals. The sections of this piece have short 'linking' passages e.g. bar 8; try and feel the sections as a whole and the linking passages as leading on to the next section.

My Favourite Things

Words by Oscar Hammerstein II. Music by Richard Rodgers

During the first night in her new job as a Nanny, Maria's horde of ill-disciplined children are all scared by a fierce thunderstorm. To soothe and calm them, Maria tells the children to think of their 'favourite things' to take their minds off the storm.

Hints & Tips: Play this piece like a bright bouncy waltz. Use plenty of staccato and take care with the fingering where there are leaps in the melody. Play smoothly when the melody moves stepwise. This approach will create musical contrast.

Bright tempo

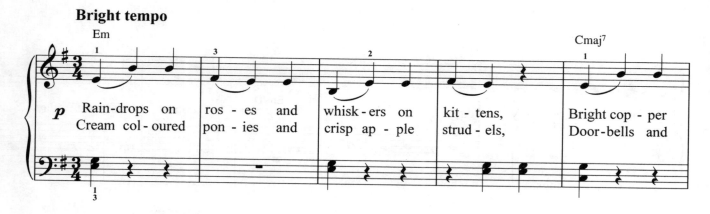

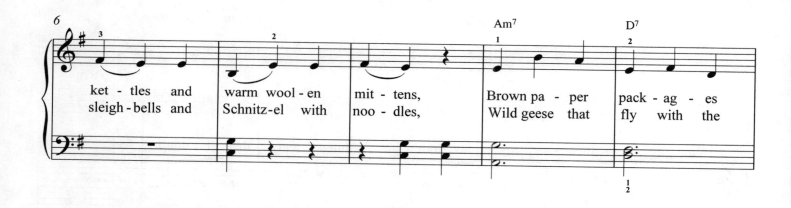

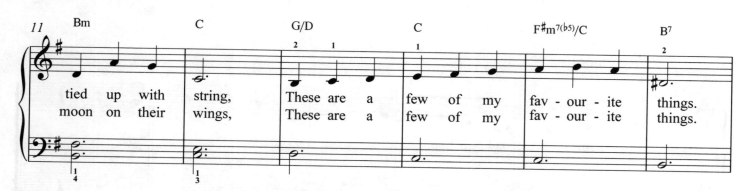

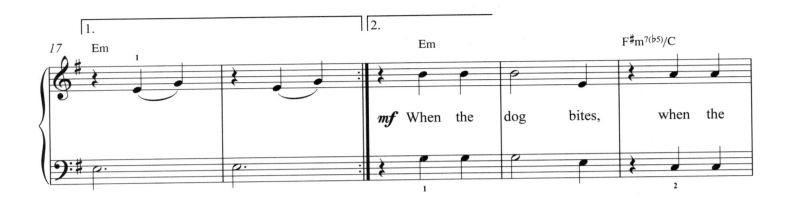

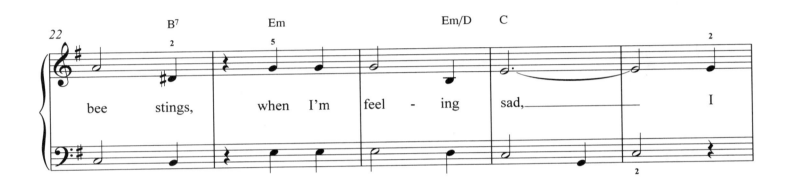

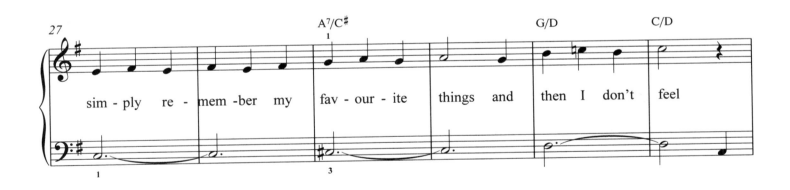

Happy Talk

Words by Oscar Hammerstein II. Music by Richard Rodgers

A huge hit in 1949 that cemented Rodgers & Hammerstein's position as the kings of Broadway. The demand for tickets was so high that theatre owners, Lee and J J Shubert, decided to add exorbitant premiums to prices charging ten times the original cost of the tickets, causing the US Government to intervene and break up the Shubert's monopoly.

Hints & Tips: Count four for this song in 2/2, until you are confident playing it. In bars 19–22 and 27–30, the left hand 'imitates' the right. Play the left hand music strongly to emphasise the imitation, and add interest to your performance.

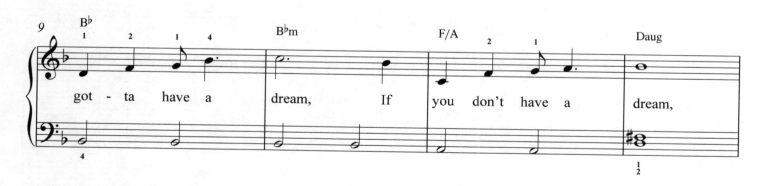

WILLY WONKA AND THE CHOCOLATE FACTORY

The Candy Man

Words & Music by Leslie Bricusse & Anthony Newley

Willy Wonka explains what you need to make delicious tasting treats. Sammy Davis Jnr made a hit record of this song, in fact, it was his only number 1 hit of Billboard's Hot 100 in 1972.

Hints & Tips: This song should have a swing feel—use the dotted rhythms to help you create this. Take special care when you count the long tied notes, and make sure you know how the repeat and coda works.

THE PHANTOM OF THE OPERA

The Music Of The Night

Music by Andrew Lloyd Webber. Words by Charles Hart

The best-known song from probably the best-known musical in the whole world. Current estimates say that over 52 million people have seen 'Phantom' worldwide.

Hints & Tips: Try to play this as sensitively and expressively as you can. Watch out for the change of time signature in bar 8.

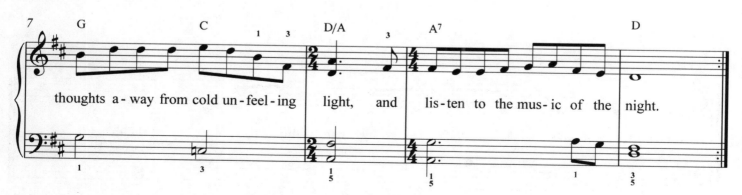

Printed in Malta by Progress Press Co. Ltd

1/07 (60880)   3 4 5 6 7 8 9